Violin
Grade 2

Pieces

for Trinity College London exams

2016-2019

Published by
Trinity College London
www.trinitycollege.com

Registered in England
Company no. 02683033
Charity no. 1014792

Printed in England by Caligraving Ltd.

Cossacks

Katherine Colledge (born 1952)
& Hugh Colledge (born 1945)

2

Fast Forward

Katherine Colledge (born 1952)
& Hugh Colledge (born 1945)

Bourrée

4th movt from Flute Sonata no. 3

Arr. Mary Cohen

George Frideric Handel
(1685–1759)

Do not play the repeats in the exam.

Tango

Neil Mackay
(1922–1973)

Rhythmico [♩ = 108]

Play the repeat in the exam.

Fiddlesticks

Sheila Nelson
(born 1936)

Singhalese Dancer

Walter Carroll
(1869–1955)

Petite Rêverie

Violin part *ed.* Mary Cohen

Adam Carse
(1878–1958)

[Blank page to facilitate page turns]

Leierkasten

Dmitri Shostakovich
(1906–1975)

Rezele

Arr. Philipp Tenta

Mordechai Gebirtig
(1877–1942)

From: Philipp Tenta: *Aus der Klezdose.*

The Kalypso Kid

Robert Trory (1945–2013) &
Sally Mays (born 1930)